"EVERYBODY WHO'S EVER BEEN LOVED BY A DOG WILL ADORE BENJI."

—Liz Smith,
Cosmopolitan

"Benji manages to express shades of love, hurt, joy and sadness so well it borders on the impossible. Throw in anxiety and fear, too."

—Phil Strassburg,
Arizona Republic

"Benji has a face far more expressive than some human actors."

—Susan Goldsmith,
American Girl Magazine

"Benji is probably the most intelligent dog in the world. Introduce him to your children by all means."

—Ann Guarino,
New York Daily News

Mulberry Square Productions
presents

A Family Film by
Joe Camp

FOR THE LOVE OF BENJI

starring
Benji
Patsy Garrett
Cynthia Smith
Allen Fiuzat

special guest star
Ed Nelson

with
Art Vasil
Peter Bowles
Bridget Armstrong
Mihalis Lambrinos

Music by Euel Box

Director of Photography Don Reddy

Original Story by
Joe Camp and Ben Vaughn

Screenplay by Joe Camp

Executive Producer Joe Camp

Produced by Ben Vaughn

Directed by Joe Camp

Filmed in Panavision
Color by CFI
A Mulberry Square Production

FOR THE LOVE OF BENJI

A Novelization by I.F. Love

From the Family Film by
Joe Camp

BANTAM BOOKS
TORONTO · NEW YORK · LONDON

FOR THE LOVE OF BENJI
A Bantam Book | June 1977

ISBN 0-553-11230-9

Published simultaneously in the United States and Canada

Bantam Books are published by Bantam Books, Inc. Its trade-
mark, consisting of the words "Bantam Books" and the por-
trayal of a bantam, is registered in the United States Patent
Office and in other countries. Marca Registrada. Bantam
Books, Inc., 666 Fifth Avenue, New York, New York 10019.

PRINTED IN THE UNITED STATES OF AMERICA

For The Love Of Benji

I

into them. When he finally
on the other side he broke into
ing the wide strip of concrete,
then he leaned up on the index of

Stelios parked his taxi and climbed out into the warm sunshine of Athens, Greece. He walked, scowling, along the noisy street toward a sidewalk café, chose a quiet table, and sat down to wait.

Soon a heavy man, wearing a food-stained apron and carrying several newspapers, entered the café. He dropped the newspapers in front of Stelios and handed him a large envelope.

"The whole world knows now," he said in a coarse voice.

Stelios glanced at the newspapers. One was Greek, one German, and one English, and they all had a picture of the same man on the front page. The headlines announced that a prominent energy scientist had disappeared in Greece.

Stelios opened the envelope and looked at the top sheet of paper. "Chandler Dietrich," he mumbled and nodded thoughtfully. Then he thumbed through several other papers, finally settling on an eight-by-ten photograph. "What's this?"

It was a picture of a woman, two children—a boy and a girl—and a dog, all staring brightly into the camera.

"The dog is the courier," the man said. "He'll be carrying the code."

"The dog! Why a dog?"

The man in the apron shrugged. "I have no idea. His name is Benji."

Stelios studied the picture again. It was a fairly small dog; a mixed breed of some kind with floppy ears and light-colored hair drooping around the eyes and off the jowls. "Who are the other people?"

"The kids' names are Paul and Cindy Chapman. They're ten and twelve years old. The woman's name is Mary Henderson. She's their governess. They'll all be changing planes in Athens tomorrow and going directly on to Crete."

Stelios sighed, taking a closer look at the brown dog. He wanted to make sure he would recognize him. There was a small tuft of white hair just behind the dog's nose, and his chest was streaked with white.

"Benji, huh?" Stelios mumbled. The man in the apron nodded. "Well, Benji, I hope you have a safe trip."

Perched on the ledge behind the back seat of the taxi, Benji couldn't have been happier as he watched the city of Houston disappear behind him. He wagged his tail and turned to look over Mary's shoulder toward the front window. He could already see a big jet plane taking off from the airfield up ahead.

It had all started about a month earlier. Paul had brought home an armload of books about Greece to read for a school assignment. Everybody in the house began looking at the books, and Dr. Chapman suddenly suggested they all go there for a vacation.

"But what'll we do with Benji and Tiffany?" Paul asked immediately.

"Well, we can't take them along," Dr. Chapman replied. "Maybe we can find someone who will board them for three weeks.

To Paul and Cindy, who had loved Benji even when he was just a floppy-eared stray with no family of his own, the suggestion couldn't have been worse. Now that Dr. Chapman had given his permission for Benji and his lady friend Tiffany to live with Paul and Cindy, they couldn't bear the thought of leaving their pets for nearly a month.

Cindy gave such strong arguments for taking them along, that the doctor finally said, "Well, let me check with the travel agent. I'll see what kind of regulations they have about taking dogs to Greece."

The taxi made a sharp turn and Benji took another look through the windshield. They were coming into the crowded airport. Cars and taxis and buses moved slowly ahead of them.

"Now let's all stick together," Mary said. "I don't want some of us ending up in Hong Kong instead of Greece."

The taxi slowed down and Benji glanced out the back window again. Then he stiffened, his eyes fixed on a fluffy cat prancing along the walk in front of the terminal buildings. A woman wearing a fur coat was attached to the leash behind the cat, and both of them had their noses up in the air. Crowds of people were moving along the walk, with men pushing cartloads of luggage between them. Benji smiled to himself. He took one more glance at the cat and then held himself ready as the taxi pulled into a parking place.

"Benji!" Paul yelled as Benji bounded through the window onto the pavement.

Benji didn't respond. He had no intention of getting lost, but cats were arrogant animals, and if you didn't let them know you were around they always seemed to think they owned the place. He let out a threatening bark and scampered across to where the woman was talking to a skycap. He skidded to a stop and gave two more loud barks.

The cat gazed indifferently at him, definitely unimpressed. Benji looked puzzled, but not for long. He suddenly felt himself scooped off the pavement.

"I'm sorry, ma'am," Paul said to the lady,

and then they were bouncing along through the crowds toward the terminal doors. "Benji, you've got to cut that out if you want to travel with us!"

Benji gave Paul's hand a lick.

"Count the bags," Mary said. "Are they all here?"

"I counted them," Cindy answered. "Have you got the tickets?"

"The tickets? Oh, dear! They must be in my purse somewhere."

They all stopped and finally breathed a sigh of relief when Mary produced the tickets. She moved into the line at the counter and Paul and Cindy stood to the side with Benji and Tiffany. Four reservations for only three people caused some confusion until Mary explained that Dr. Chapman would be coming a week later, and the ticket clerk went off to check the computers.

"We're going to Greece," Mary said to the man standing behind her.

He was a tall, handsome man with a little gray hair at the temples. He smiled politely. "So am I."

"You are?" Mary said with surprise.

"That's the only place this airline goes."

"Oh," Mary said, "of course." She looked off behind the counter and then turned back to the man. "I'm sorry this is taking so long. Where in Greece are you going?"

"I'm going to Crete," the man said politely.

"Really? That's where we're going."

The man smiled. "It's a beautiful island. I've been there many times. I'll be happy to tell you the good places to go. My name is Chandler Dietrich, by the way."

Mary smiled and shook his hand. "I'm Mary Henderson, and this is Paul and Cynthia Chapman. And that's Benji and Tiffany."

Just then a pretty girl in an airline uniform came up and asked Cindy for the names of her dogs. Cindy told her, adding that they were going to Crete.

"Well, I'm sure you're going to have a very nice trip, Benji and Tiffany," the girl said. She carefully wrote their names on two tags.

"Are you sure they'll be all right?" Cindy asked.

"They'll be just fine. My cat travels this way all the time."

"Tiffany hasn't been feeling well," Cindy said. "She sort of has a condition."

"Well, we'll take good care of her. I promise you that."

The girl had the tags attached to the cages now and she put Tiffany gently inside hers and locked it up. Benji took a final look at Paul and Cindy and then allowed himself to be lifted from the counter and locked into the cage.

"See you in Crete," Paul called out to both

of them and they were placed on a conveyor belt.

The two dogs passed into a narrow corridor, and the noises of the front terminal suddenly disappeared. The dogs moved through a small hole and into a huge baggage room. Now Benji could hear the whine of jet engines and the clatter of machinery and trucks. He settled down and rested his chin on the bottom of the cage. Then he looked up quickly.

Dietrich, the man who had been in line behind Mary, was coming toward him, walking fast alongside the conveyor belt. He rested his hand on top of the cage and peered in. "Hi there, Benji boy," he said.

Benji gave him a panting smile of recognition, then he felt his cage being lifted from the conveyor belt and they were moving away. He wondered why the man hadn't taken Tiffany too.

They passed through a door into a room that was crowded with noisy machinery. Dietrich placed the cage on a counter and slid a steel pin into the lock. Benji wagged his tail. Perhaps he was going to be let out of the cage. But the door stayed shut.

Benji watched as Dietrich opened the top of a tiny bottle and poured some liquid onto his handkerchief.

"OK, Benji, now just relax. This won't take long and it won't hurt a bit."

Benji hesitated as the man opened the door. Then he tried to turn his head away as the man grabbed his neck and held the handkerchief tightly to his nose.

Benji had never smelled anything like it. The powerful vapor stung his nostrils and made him feel dizzy. He dug his paws into the bottom of the cage and twisted with all his strength, trying to wrench his head loose. But his legs seemed to buckle under him and suddenly his whole body went limp.

He was flat on the bottom of the cage now and everything in the room was floating around, going in and out of focus. Mr. Dietrich had brought something shiny from his pocket and Benji blinked woozily, trying to see what it was. Then he felt his paw lifted and the pad of his foot was pressed hard against the cold metal of the object.

"There you go, Benji. That wasn't so bad, was it?"

The man was holding a match to the piece of metal now. It flamed away into nothing. The cage door came shut again, the lock rattling back into place. Dietrich peered in and smiled. "Good boy, Benji. I'll see you in Crete in about twelve hours, huh?"

Benji felt himself being carried back through the door and bounced down onto the conveyor belt. Then Mr. Dietrich was gone and Benji was moving along the belt, his head resting between his paws, blinking woozily.

"Here's another dog," somebody said. Benji's cage was lifted again, and placed on a big baggage cart. A couple of minutes later the cart was towed out into the sunshine and Benji closed his eyes. All he wanted to do now was sleep.

II

The flight from Athens down to the island of Crete took less than half an hour, but the scenery was magnificent. The plane was only half full, so all of them except Mr. Dietrich had window seats and a good view.

The color of the water was amazing: a rich azure that turned to lacy white around the hundreds of islands. It was even prettier than the postcards and travel brochures they had studied back in Silver Creek. Then, as the plane approached the island of Crete, the little whitewashed villages along the coast looked no different from how they must have looked centuries earlier.

Mr. Dietrich seemed to know the island of Crete very well, and told them about the interesting archaeological sites there. But because they had now been traveling for well over twelve hours, Paul and Cindy slept through a good part of the history lesson. Now the famous island was directly beneath them and the plane turned and seemed to slow down almost to a stop as they started the descent toward the airport.

The airport at Crete was small compared to the one in Athens, and the passengers had to walk several hundred yards to the terminal building.

"As soon as you're all settled and catch up on your sleep," Mr. Dietrich said to Mary, "I'm treating all three of you to the best meal you've ever had in your lives."

Mary hesitated, then said, "You really don't have to do that, Mr. Dietrich. I'm sure you have other important business to attend to."

Mr. Dietrich shook his head. "I won't have it any other way. I want you to see the best of Crete."

Mary smiled, not wanting to protest too vigorously.

"Will it be Greek food?" Paul asked.

"Very Greek."

"What's Greek food like?" Cindy asked suspiciously.

"I will promise you only one thing," Mr. Dietrich laughed. "There won't be any fried chicken on the menu."

Paul laughed, but Cindy thought fried chicken sounded pretty good right now.

A young man in an Olympic Airways uniform was just inside the door holding a blackboard with Mr. Dietrich's name chalked on it. Cindy was the only one who noticed.

"Mr. Dietrich, look at that!"

He glanced at the board and stopped abruptly. "Can you believe that? I guess there's no escaping. Why don't you all go on ahead to the baggage claim area. I'll be right there."

When they moved off Dietrich turned quickly to the man. "I'm Chandler Dietrich, young man," he said in fluent Greek.

The messenger searched his pockets and brought out a folded piece of paper. "A man left this message for you, sir. He said it was urgent."

Dietrich unfolded the paper and frowned as he studied the message. "Did he leave his name?"

"No, sir."

Dietrich nodded and handed him a tip. Then he moved into the terminal building, angling off toward the baggage area where Mary, Paul, and Cindy were watching the luggage come through on a conveyor belt.

"Is anything wrong?" Mary asked when she saw his dark look.

"Uh . . . no. No, not at all. I just have to make a phone call." He smiled to reassure them. "Look, why don't you and the kids wait for the luggage and the dogs . . ." He searched his pockets for his claim check. "And if you don't mind, watch for my bag too. It's a light tan, about so big."

"Sure," Paul said, "we'll find it."

"I'd appreciate it, Paul. I'll be back in a minute and then we'll all take a cab together so you won't have to fight the language problem."

"That'd be great," Mary smiled. "Thank you."

"Thank *you*," Dietrich said with a smile, and strode off.

He moved along to the last pay phone in the line and stopped, glancing casually at the OUT OF ORDER sign taped across it. He consulted the note again and paced impatiently near the phone for a half minute. Suddenly it rang. He quickly lifted the receiver, and said, "Dietrich."

A cold and menacing voice answered him. "Welcome to Crete, Mr. Dietrich. Do you have the coordinate code?"

"I have it. It's in a safe place."

"Good. You will find the map in an envelope taped under the shelf below the phone."

Dietrich bent forward and spotted the bulky envelope. He tore it loose and took the map from inside. "I have it."

"Very good. The project is getting out of hand, Mr. Dietrich, so waste no time. Signal if you need help. We will be watching you."

"I won't need any help," Dietrich said irritably, "and I don't need to be watched. I'm perfectly capable of handling this alone."

The phone clicked softly and Dietrich rattled the hook. "Hello?"

The man had hung up. Dietrich banged the receiver down and quickly slid the map into his inside coat pocket. Then he looked out at the people crisscrossing the terminal lobby. He recognized none of them, and there seemed to be no one watching him. Then he looked up sharply at the mezzanine.

There standing by another bank of pay phones was a dark, thick-necked Greek. His cold, penetrating eyes seemed to be gazing idly down at the crowds. It was Stelios.

Dietrich wondered if he was the man who had been assigned to watch him. Or was he the man who had just called him? Or was he just another passenger killing time between flights?

Mary and the kids all looked worried when Dietrich got back to the baggage area. They were the only ones still standing by the conveyor belt and Mary turned quickly when she saw him.

"Chandler! I'm so glad you're back. They're not here! All the luggage came, but there's no sign of Benji or Tiffany!"

"What?" Dietrich snapped. His eyes showed real concern. "Are you sure?"

"We've watched everything that came in," Paul said. "They're just not here."

Dietrich glanced around and found the customer service counter. "They must be here somewhere!" He moved quickly to the counter with Mary and the kids following close behind.

"Excuse me, there's supposed to be two dogs on the flight from Athens. Is it possible they haven't brought them in yet?"

"No," the man said. He glanced at the baggage area. "They would be coming through there, the same as the luggage. Are you sure they were loaded in Athens?"

Dietrich explained that they had come from Houston and then caught the first flight from Athens to Crete.

The man smiled. "Well, I'm sure they're all right. They probably missed the plane change in Athens." He glanced at Paul and Cindy. "Now please don't worry. I'll go call and find out for sure. And I promise they'll get the best of care, and be on the next flight."

"When is the next flight?" Mary asked.

"Tomorrow morning."

"Oh, my," Mary groaned. And the customer service man vanished around a corner. "I think I'll go with him," Dietrich said, glancing after the man, "just to be sure."

"Mr. Dietrich!" Mary called as he hurried off, "be sure to tell them they haven't had anything to eat or drink in almost twelve hours!"

"And that Tiffany has a condition!" Cindy added.

Mary sighed as they waited. "I guess we'd better gather up our bags."

"What if they don't find them?" Cindy asked as they moved back to the conveyor belt. "What if they're still in Houston?"

"I'm sure they must be in Athens, sweetheart. Don't worry. If they're not on the flight tomorrow we'll go back to Athens and get them."

"Anyway," Paul said trying to bolster Cindy's spirits, "they're probably having a big time at the Athens Airport. Benji knows how to take care of himself."

Twenty feet away, Stelios folded his newspaper, studied Mary, Paul, and Cindy for a quick moment, then moved casually from the ticket counter.

For the tenth time in the last hour, Benji's stomach growled and twisted, reminding him that he was hungry. Even a drink of water would help. The liquid Dietrich had held to his nose in Houston had made his mouth and throat feel dry as dust.

When he and Tiffany were unloaded from the plane, Benji expected to see Mary, Paul, and Cindy smiling at him, but all he had seen was another cart piled high with suitcases. Then they were towed off to a big room.

Their cages were side by side on a counter, and Benji could hear Tiffany's low whimper, but he had no way of seeing her. Perhaps that was just as well because Tiffany looked terrible. She had barked and whimpered until she was exhausted, and now her head rested between her paws as she gazed forlornly out at the stacks of bags and boxes.

Somewhere across the room a bell rang

. . . and continued ringing repeatedly. Peering between two stacks of suitcases, Benji saw a man in coveralls pick up the telephone.

The man nodded as he listened. Then he frowned and looked off into the room.

He left the receiver dangling and soon Benji saw him moving up the aisle, looking under counters and between suitcases. Benji came quickly to his feet and barked. Then his heart jumped. The man was looking directly at him, a big smile coming to his face.

The man held up a finger and said something Benji couldn't understand and then went back to the phone. Benji turned a quick circle in his cage, his tail wagging happily, and then he moaned and yelped at Tiffany.

She came to her feet and shook herself awake. Benji peered through the suitcases again and saw the man hang up the phone.

A minute later he was smiling and carrying a bowl of water as he came up the aisle. Benji barked excitedly. They were saved! The man grinned and said something to Tiffany. Then he set the water on the counter and said something in Greek to Benji.

Benji cocked his head, listening carefully. The man's voice sounded sympathetic, but Benji couldn't make any sense out of the words. Then the man frowned and pulled at the lock on Benji's cage. He muttered some more of the strange sounds and checked Tiffany's lock.

Benji's hopes suddenly plummeted as the

man moved off again, leaving the water just outside Benji's cage.

Benji watched the man go past the telephone and disappear. Then he stared at the clear, cool liquid only six inches from his nose. Water had never looked quite so good to him. He could almost taste it. He moved his nose as close to the wire cage as he could and thrust his tongue through one of the holes.

It was hopeless—he was at least an inch short. He shifted, trying another hole, but he still couldn't reach. Benji sighed and stretched out, resting his chin on the bottom of the cage.

He turned his paw and frowned at it, seeing nothing particularly unusual on the pad where Mr. Dietrich pressed the metal. There were some tiny marks; a little square of dots that was hardly visible. Benji licked his paw, tasting nothing. But the marks didn't come off. He licked at it again and then gave it up, resting his head on the bottom of the cage again.

Ten minutes passed and Benji finally closed his eyes. The man would come back, he told himself—he just had to be patient. He sighed heavily and waited another ten minutes. Then he heard a door swing open and got up instantly.

The man came up the aisle again, carrying a huge pair of clippers. Benji wagged his tail and barked. Tiffany also rose, panting heavily with anticipation.

The man laughed, talking to both of them

as he gripped the lock between the jaws of the clippers. With one movement he squeezed the handles together and the lock snapped and dropped to the counter. The man's face brightened and he laughed again as he reached for the clasp of the cage. Then he hesitated, muttering something as he looked off at the corner of the room.

The telephone was ringing again.

Benji gave the man a hopeful look, but it did no good. The man was moving away, shouting something at the telephone as he strode back down the aisle.

Benji watched the man lift the telephone receiver and start talking. He pushed his nose gently against the door of the cage. It moved!

Benji pushed again. Slowly he nudged the door open enough to squeeze his nose through, then his whole head. In his earnestness to open the door, he failed to notice the bowl of water now teetering precariously on the edge of the counter.

The crash of shattering pottery sounded like an explosion as the bowl hit the concrete floor.

What happened in the next two minutes happened so fast, Benji wasn't sure what to make of it. As quickly as the water dish shattered he heard a shout from the man at the telephone. And then the man was gone from the phone and striding up the aisle. Benji stood on the counter ready to dash. As the man approached, suddenly his foot slipped on the wet pavement and the cage and Benji and the man all tumbled to the floor in a tangled heap.

Benji scrambled to his feet and moved fast. The man was shouting angrily and then groaning as he got to his hands and knees. By then Benji was under a different counter twenty feet away, watching, not certain what to do next. Then a nearby door swung open and another man was peering in.

"I say, is this the baggage storage area?" he asked with a decidedly British accent. "Do you speak English?" the Britisher continued, not seeming to notice that the luggage man was still sprawled on the concrete floor.

"You see, I'm looking for a . . ."

Suddenly the luggage man shouted and gestured wildly toward Benji. Benji bolted for the door, running right between the Britisher's legs.

"My word—what was that?" he heard the man cry as Benji raced past a woman who shrieked, "Ronald, it's him! It's the dog!"

Benji didn't go far. After about fifty feet he skidded to a stop on the slippery floor and ducked quickly into an opening under a vacant ticket counter. Then he peered back around the corner.

The Britisher was sitting spread-legged on the floor, having been run down by the baggage man as he rushed after Benji. A woman ran toward him shouting, "It's the dog! Come on!" as she helped the Britisher to his feet.

She was a pretty woman with blond hair and dressed in a neat suit. But Benji decided not to take any chances as all three of them came racing toward him.

"Here, doggie! Don't be frightened, doggie!" the Englishman was calling out behind him.

Benji glanced back and then searched for an escape route. He saw several open doors, but they all looked suspicious. Then he saw one leading into a huge room with tables and a lot of people standing by opened luggage. He made a sharp turn and dashed around the left side of the room.

A man in a uniform turned sharply from the suitcases he was inspecting and shouted something, but Benji kept moving.

The baggage man raced through the door followed by the English couple. They circled around behind Benji. The Englishman smiled and said something to the man in uniform, looking off toward Benji.

"Come on, doggie!" the Englishman shouted.

When he reached the far side of the room Benji stopped and waited, catching his breath for a minute. There appeared to be no good escape route from the room. Then, with the three pursuers almost upon him, he barreled straight across the middle of the room and out the door they had come in.

"Blast!" shouted the Englishman.

Benji glanced around some more as he trotted through the crowded lobby.

"Would you catch my little dog, please?" pleaded the Englishwoman, looking anxiously for help. Her voice sounded sweet and innocent, as if she were some little girl in distress trying to get her pet back.

Benji picked up a little speed and quickly spotted a narrow door standing half open. It was risky, but Benji decided he'd better take the chance.

Behind the door a narrow corridor ran for a hundred feet and then turned. If there was a closed door at the other end, he was going to be in big trouble. He moved faster, trying desperately to outrun the approaching footsteps behind him. Then as he turned the corner his heart jumped. Daylight! And lots of wide-open space.

Eight or ten huge jet airplanes were standing just outside the building, some of them with their engines screeching and whining. There were also a lot of men in coveralls, and three or four trucks crossing the area. Benji took it in with a glance and darted along under the first airplane, heading up the line toward the end of the building. A man shouted, but Benji paid no attention.

A man in a uniform stopped the English couple and was motioning them back toward the corridor. But the baggage man was still coming. Benji watched, catching his breath for a minute, not too worried about the one man catching him in all that open space. The English couple looked upset as the uniformed man shooed them back into the corridor. And the baggage man was puffing hard.

In the other direction, at the far end of the terminal building, a high iron fence ran along the side of the airport runway. But the bars of the fence were wide enough for Benji to easily squeeze through. He threw a final glance at the baggage man and darted across the runway, eased his way through the fence, and disappeared into the traffic beyond.

III

Benji had followed the traffic into downtown Athens, and he had never been in such a crowded place. The sidewalk was a moving tangle of legs and tramping feet, making it impossible to walk in a straight line. He trotted into the gutter now and then before he could find a few inches to slip back into the crowd.

The noise was even worse. Everybody in a car seemed to honk constantly, and in front of every store and shop people were laughing and talking and shouting at each other with their hands and arms waving in all directions. Like the man in the baggage room, their words sounded strange.

He had tried to find some food in a couple of trash cans. The first one had nothing but paper and dirt and splintered pieces of wood, and somebody shooed him out of it the second before he had a chance to get to the bottom of it. Then he had seen a bunch of people sitting at tables next to the sidewalk and his hopes had lifted a little. Most of them only had cups in front of them, or they were sipping some colored liquid out of little glasses. But he had moved among the tables until he sniffed something good, and then he sat down, his tail wagging frantically. The man had reached over and patted his head, and then the woman was smiling and taking something from her plate. But then another man was yelling from inside, rushing out at him and flapping his apron. Benji had ducked around to the other side of the table close to the woman, but the man with the apron followed him, his voice harsh and threatening. Benji knew he wasn't wanted. He hung his head and moved on.

The terrible part was all the water he saw on those tables next to the sidewalk. He had passed five or six such places, and almost every one had glasses and pitchers of water all over the place, and he had seen one of the waiters emptying glasses into the dirt under a potted plant. He stopped briefly, panting up at the man, hoping for just a few drops. But the man looked right past him, staring off at something across the street, and then returning to the café with the empty glasses.

Benji finally stopped walking. He climbed up onto a large windowsill which ran in front of a store window filled with toys. In both directions there were more buildings and more traffic and more people scurrying along the sidewalk. He looked around for a minute and finally dropped his chin in exhaustion. Back home in

Silver Creek, he had always known where to find a scrap of food or a cool drink of water. But here, wherever "here" was, he only knew that he was hungry and thirsty and suddenly very lonely.

Suddenly Benji snapped to attention, his eyes riveted on a young girl with blond hair who was getting out of a taxi. An older lady also emerged and took the younger girl by the arm. Benji barked loudly, leaped onto the sidewalk, and raced frantically down the street, determined not to lose them. He scurried past pedestrians, twisting around legs and jumping over feet. He skidded to a stop, as his last bark died in his throat.

It was not Cindy. The girl was staring down at him, blinking and backing away. The older lady standing next to her yelled at Benji and waved her arms for him to get away. Benji couldn't understand any of her words, but the meaning was clear. He turned and moved dejectedly on down the street.

It came suddenly, and Benji was so surprised he couldn't believe it for a minute. He had turned a corner and walked slowly along with pedestrians for another block, and then they had all stopped to wait for a traffic light. When he looked up, there it was across the street—a huge fountain with plumes of water shooting high in the air and dropping into a big pond. Benji blinked, then blinked again. His dry

33

tongue quivered. It was the most beautiful thing he had ever seen.

The light changed and he moved along with the crowd, making sure no cars were turning the corner into them. When he finally reached the curb on the other side he broke into a full run, crossing the wide strip of concrete, then the grass, then he leaped up on the ledge at the side of the pond. He took a couple of steps, balancing himself, and then he was drinking, lapping greedily at the cool, delicious liquid.

It was the best water Benji had ever tasted. Even better than the water he and Tiffany used to share from the old birdbath in the Silver Creek park. Benji reached to lap up some more, but before his tongue could reach the water, he suddenly found himself airborne.

The two strong hands which had interrupted him belonged to a policeman who dropped him back down onto the sidewalk. The policeman spoke sternly to Benji and shook his finger in Benji's confused face. Benji took one long last look at the huge fountain. He'd only wanted a drink.

Benji moped along, dodging feet, circling around in the gutter to pass the more crowded spots. His stomach ached with hunger. He thought of Bill's café back in Silver Creek where he could always manage a handout, and he remembered his favorite trash can in the park. He had no idea where he was, but surely they must have trash cans. At the corner he turned up a narrower street and ducked into the alley that he knew must run behind the many cafés.

A hundred feet into the alley, Benji pulled up short. A huge truck had turned into the other end of the alley and seemed to be coming at full speed, its motor roaring and gears clashing, and it filled the whole width of space between the buildings. Benji edged to the side, but the truck's big tires were scraping along only inches from the brick wall. He backed away a couple steps, uncertain what to do. Then a deafening blast suddenly sounded through the narrow alley, and Benji was running, charging out of the alley as if he had been shot from a cannon.

He didn't stop or even slow down when he reached the street but sped across the bigger boulevard. With the sound of the truck's horn still ringing in his ears, he headed for the hills he had seen behind the city. For the time being, he had seen enough of downtown Athens.

He was dashing across weedy fields of what appeared to be a collection of very old stones and statues before he finally slowed down a little and took his bearings.

On the hill above him there were a lot of old buildings that looked as if they had been shaken to the ground by a big earthquake. A few columns were still standing, but for the most part they looked like piles of rubble, with a lot of statues and carved slabs of marble lying around. Benji finally stopped and caught his breath while he took another look at the city below.

He was no longer so certain now about getting something to eat. This place was a lot bigger than Silver Creek, and maybe the place was so big and had so many people there just weren't any scraps left over for dogs. For a minute Benji wondered if he would ever find Mary, Paul, and Cindy. Maybe he would end up starving to death far from home.

He sighed wearily and glanced around. It was possible, he supposed, that there might be something to eat in these fields.

He finally moved on, sniffing at a few of the statues and fallen slabs of marble. They smelled old. He climbed up some fallen rocks and went over a wall, suddenly finding himself in a graveyard. That too smelled old, and some of the gravestones were so worn that the lettering was almost invisible. Benji gave them a couple of sniffs and trotted along, working his way toward the higher ground at the back. Then he suddenly stopped, sniffing the air.

Did he smell meat? It seemed like it, and the smell came from directly ahead. But it was hard to believe that there could be anything to eat in a place like this. He sniffed again and trotted on, following the scent. Then he came to an abrupt halt, his heart leaping to his throat.

There was food—a big, juicy bone about a foot and a half long, with ragged chunks of delicious-looking meat hanging from all sides of it. There was also a pair of jaws working on it, and attached to the jaws was the biggest dog Benji had ever seen in his life.

Benji was only ten feet away, and surely the animal had noticed him. But he didn't seem to be paying any attention—or at least he wasn't worried about it. He was lying in a kind of nook, with stone walls on both sides of him, and another wall against the hillside behind. One of his huge paws was resting over the bone and his eyes were half closed, not paying any attention to much of anything as he gnawed and chomped away.

Benji would have settled for one tiny corner of the bone, or even one of the good-sized chunks of meat hanging from all sides of it. But he had very little experience with unfriendly dogs. If this dog proved to be unfriendly, he could probably break half of Benji's bones with one bite.

Benji glanced to the sides and to the top of the wall behind the dog. It might be safe up there. He took one more look at the bone and licked his chops. Then, keeping a wary eye on the big dog, he trotted off to the side and scampered up the hill.

He was ten or twelve feet above the animal when he reached the top of the wall behind the nook. He stood looking down at him for a minute and then gave a friendly woof and wagged his tail as if to say "Hello there." Then he wagged his tail, waiting for the dog to glance up.

Could he be deaf? More likely he just didn't care to waste his time with Benji. But what Benji lacked in size, he made up for in persistence. He tried again, making his woof a little louder this time.

There was still no answer, or any indication that the animal had heard him. Benji watched for a couple of more minutes and finally moved to the edge of the wall. From there he bounded down to a ledge only three or four feet above the other dog. He barked again.

He might as well have been talking to the wall. There was no question about it—the dog was not friendly. On the other hand, he didn't appear to be mean or vicious either. So what should he do now? The dog certainly wouldn't miss one or two little scraps from his bone. But Benji could hardly jump down there and just grab them. If the big dog knew how hungry he was, and that it was a matter of life and death, would he be more cooperative? Benji glanced restlessly at the top of the wall and back to the dog. He would make one more try, he decided, and moving to the front of the ledge, he jumped down beside the dog, landing as softly as he could. Then he froze, holding his breath for a minute.

The dog was looking at him, his huge head twisted, his jaws dripping saliva, staring at Benji with a faint frown on his face. From the look the dog was giving him, Benji might have been an ant or a water bug, and he was wondering if it was worth the bother to squash him under his paw. Benji opened his mouth and panted, hesitantly wagging his tail.

The big dog didn't appear to be impressed. Without so much as a grunt or a sniff, he returned his attention to the bone.

Benji snorted. If he weren't so hungry, he would have trotted off without a backward glance. But this close the bone smelled twice as good, and his stomach was gurgling and grumbling so loud he couldn't believe the big dog didn't hear it. Benji moved cautiously forward and dropped to his belly, inching alongside the dog's huge shoulder and then to within licking distance of the bone. For a full minute he lay there, watching, listening to the rough scraping of teeth and the hissing and snorting of the big animal's breathing. Finally he stretched out as far as he could reach and gingerly touched a morsel of meat with his tongue.

The bone was gone in the same instant. Without giving Benji a glance the big dog clamped his jaws over it, pulled himself up and turned completely around, plopping his tail right into Benji's face.

It was really very rude and Benji still didn't understand as he trotted back to town. After all, he would have never hesitated a minute to share his food with a stranger. In fact, that's exactly how he and Tiffany had met several years earlier. But that time she had been the one who was starving and Benji had shared his big, juicy bone with her. Dogs must be different over here.

On the way back, Benji kept to the narrower streets, making a quick check of trash cans, pausing only briefly at a couple of doors where there was the smell of food.

There was a strong scent coming from somewhere in the town and he let his nose be his guide, moving deeper into the narrow streets of the city. The scent was growing stronger and suddenly there it was.

He had never seen anything like it back home. In Silver Creek all the markets were inside of buildings, with hissing glass doors and signs and lights. But standing before him now was a whole block full of small open booths, every one of them displaying some kind of food. There were fresh fruits and vegetables and candies and breads and cakes and cookies. In other booths there were things in boxes and cans, while others were stacked high with fish. The smells were incredible, and Benji sat down and licked his chops as he looked the place over. From where he was sitting he could see three meat booths, every one of them packed with all kinds of delicious-looking chunks of meat. Meat was hanging from hooks and resting on counters and packed on shelves and some of the pieces were absolutely huge.

Benji's gaze finally settled on the closest booth. A customer was standing in front of it holding a long string of sausages, waving it around as he talked to the man behind the counter. It looked as if they were having an argument of some kind. But the sausages looked delicious, and Benji couldn't keep his eyes off them. He moved closer, making a broad circle through the crowd, and his eyes suddenly spotted some juicy-looking scraps beneath the counter.

He glanced at the arguing men and then carefully slipped under the counter and proceeded to help himself, completely ignoring the argument, which was growing steadily in both volume and intensity.

The customer seemed to underline each loud complaint with a wild gesture which appeared all the more dramatic because of the long string of sausages held tightly in his fist.

Benji suddenly looked up. The irate customer had accidentally dropped one end of the sausage string and it was now dangling right in front of Benji's face. A veritable feast. His heart was in his throat as he watched the sausages swing back and forth. Should he or shouldn't he? Of course he shouldn't but he was rapidly getting to the point where he couldn't help himself.

As the customer pounded the table top, the long string of sausages once again began to rotate slowly in front of Benji. He couldn't resist a sniff. They must be delicious! Benji glanced up at the customer, still embroiled in the heated conversation. Benji's stomach ached and his mouth watered. The temptation was just too great.

Like a flash, Benji leaped forward, snatched the sausages, and took off at full speed, the wind tearing past his face. Behind him, he heard an angry cry. Then a second and a third man were shouting and suddenly people in front of him were turning and looking as he sped by. The sausages were bounding along behind him, sometimes flying over his head and whipping back, but he didn't break his stride. He was out on a sidewalk making a sharp turn, scooting between the legs of a woman carrying a basket, then bounding off down a long sidewalk. The woman screamed and Benji heard the basket crash to the ground.

If he had looked back, he would have seen a very curious sight. The customer and the meat man were standing in the middle of the street laughing uproariously. It suddenly seemed quite humorous that a little dog like Benji could throw an entire market into such an uproar. In fact, the more they thought about it, the funnier it seemed. Soon, they were both bent over double with laughter and curious pedestrians were casting puzzled glances their way.

Suddenly a small sports car screeched to a halt right behind them. The driver looked off down the street, trying to spot Benji among the crowd.

"I'm almost positive it was him," he said. His companion insisted that they must continue looking. It was the British couple who had so recently chased him through the airport.

The big brown dog was in the same spot, still facing the wall and chewing on the same bone as when Benji had left him. Benji trotted up the slope and made himself comfortable. Then he bit casually into the first sausage as if it was just one more ordinary meal.

After a minute or so he heard the other dog quit gnawing on the bone and sniff the air. Then he saw the big head turn and the eyes glance from the sausages to himself. Benji paid no attention. He glanced off at the scenery while he chewed, and then he bit into his second sausage.

The big dog finally rose. The huge body came up and the big head and dripping jowls were towering over Benji for a moment as the animal turned and sat down, staring at the sausages now. Benji chewed for a few more seconds and then glanced up indifferently as if noticing the dog for the first time.

There seemed to be a slight frown on the dog's face as he stretched out again and stared. Benji chewed a little longer and finally gave the animal a look of mild surprise as if suddenly realizing his friend might be interested in a bit of sausage to go along with his bone.

Benji didn't hesitate. He was a gracious, friendly, and generous dog, and unlike some others he had met, the last thing he would consider would be to hog all of the food for himself. As if it were the most ordinary thing in the world, he picked up the other end of the sausage string and dropped it on the ground very near the other dog.

The big animal stared at him for a minute as if he couldn't quite believe it and Benji smiled to himself as he went back to his end of the sausage string and resumed eating.

IV

The sun was shining brilliantly when Benji finally awakened the next morning. He stirred uneasily, his paw twitching; he was having vague dreams about Mr. Dietrich. Then he was whimpering, and suddenly he was awake, blinking across the graveyard and the ruins at the sun-drenched city of Athens.

He yawned, stretching his mouth wide, and looked around for his friend. There was no one in sight. The big brown dog had slept at the back of the nook, taking up almost the entire width between the two side walls, and Benji had curled up near his head. But now he was alone.

Benji moved out to the edge of the nook where he could see into the graveyard and on the hill behind. Other than some birds chirping and a rooster crowing somewhere in the distance, there was nobody around. He stretched his back legs and dug at a flea just behind his ear. Then he scampered up to the top of the hill to look off toward the city again and his eyes suddenly brightened.

Quite a distance away and moving up some

steps that led into the city, his big brown dog friend was loping along with the air of somebody just starting out on his day's business.

Benji moved fast, running down through the graveyard and over the wall into the ruins. He scampered through the statues and marble slabs and then up the steps where he had last seen the big dog. When he reached the sidewalk he stopped and looked quickly around.

The big dog was nowhere in sight. Shopkeepers were opening up for the day, greeting each other across the street; people were getting on buses, while others read newspapers as they walked along. Benji looked in every direction before he finally gave it up.

He was a little disappointed. He had hoped his new friend would show him around, but the big dog probably had more pressing affairs to take care of. Benji took one last look, then trotted off, glancing at faces and giving a quick check to side streets as he started his search.

There weren't many people sitting in the sidewalk cafés that hour, and the loitering waiters all give him cold looks. So Benji moved on, heading down to the open marketplace where he had found the sausages.

Things seemed to be busier than ever. Truckloads of food were being unloaded and taken to the booths, and customers with net bags were crowding through the aisles between the stalls. Benji kept his distance for a few minutes studying the situation.

The proprietor of the meat booth with the sausages was out in front of his stall sweeping a pile of trash out of the aisle. Benji watched him and then moved toward one of the other meat booths, keeping an eye on the man with the broom. Halfway there, the man looked up and Benji trotted quickly to a position behind a stack of crated lettuce. When he peered out the man was sweeping again. Benji gave him a final glance and moved forward, enjoying the mouth-watering aromas.

The shout from behind him came like a bolt of lightning, and Benji's heart almost leaped from his chest. All Benji saw was a quick glimpse of the man from the sausage booth moving quickly toward him. The man had a grin on his face and was waving something in his hand. For a split second Benji thought it looked like a huge meaty bone, but he wasn't about to risk a closer look.

"*Ela! Ela!*" the man called after him. Benji took off at full speed down the edge of the crowded aisle.

He heard the man scream again, but he didn't look back. He swerved in and out of feet and around packing crates. He slipped and skidded as he tried to turn and avoid a man carrying a huge basket on his shoulder. There was a yell and a crash and Benji was suddenly in a sea of fresh oranges and the man was sprawled on his belly. He shook his fist at Benji and yelled violently.

Benji raced under the booths and up another aisle, going between legs, or around them, or anyplace he could see daylight. He had an ominous feeling he was in big trouble this time, and his escape wasn't going to be so easy.

He heard more things crash to the ground behind him and more people joined the shouting. He skidded to a halt and reversed his direction again. Two men were coming at him, both crouched low to prevent his getting past. Then he faced another crowd, some of the people yelling at him and some reaching out as he tried to get by.

Benji turned under a booth and scampered out into what seemed like a clear escape route into the open plaza. Suddenly something flashed by in front of his face. He was stopped cold, twisting and tangled in a heavy net. He groped at it, turning and trying to run the other way, but the efforts only made things worse. He looked up.

Towering above him were two very tall policemen. One was wagging his finger at him, and the other was speaking very harshly. Benji hung his head for a minute and then gave the man a panting smile, hoping for a similar response. The man only frowned and didn't lift the net.

The two policemen didn't seem to understand or put much trust in the friendly barks and tail wagging Benji gave them. They kept him tightly closed in the net until a van showed up. Then a uniformed man transferred him to a cage in the back of the van and he was driven away. Ten minutes later a man looked closely at his collar and made some notes, and he was placed in a big cage with a dozen other dogs barking and yelping all around him.

A man came with a bowl of water and put it in the cage. Benji enjoyed the drink, and wished for a little food to go with it. He joined in the barking for a while. Then he gave it up and put his head on the ground, watching the door at the back of the building. Things looked bad, he reflected. Now he was going to find out what they did with homeless dogs in Greece.

Mary held the telephone receiver down for a moment and then picked it up and dialed for the tenth time in the last half hour. She groaned inwardly as the voice answered in Greek.

"Do you happen to speak English?" she asked, speaking slowly and distinctly.

There was a silence at the other end, then the halting voice said, "One minutes, if you pliss."

Less than half of the places she had called were able to find anyone who could speak to her in English, and she'd had to hang up not knowing if they had Benji or not.

"Maybe we just ought to get in a taxicab and ride around looking for him," Paul said now as Mary waited.

"You might be right, Paul. But there are

only three more dog pounds listed in the book. We can ..."

She turned quickly back to the phone as she heard someone pick up the receiver at the other end.

"May I help you, madam? I speak English."

Mary breathed a sigh or relief. "Yes . . . that is, I hope you can help us. You see, we're American tourists, and we brought two dogs to Greece, and when we transferred flights to go to Crete one of the dogs ..."

"Is the dog's name Benji, madam?"

Mary almost dropped the phone. *"Yes,"* she cried, "Do you have him there? Do you know where he is? Is he all right?"

"He's fine. He was brought in about twenty minutes ago."

Paul and Cindy were both hovering over her now, their eyes shining. "They've found him," Mary quickly told them.

"We'll be over to get him right away," she told the man. "Are you sure he's all right?"

"Quite sure, madam. Don't worry."

"Oh, thank you so much. I'll . . . oh, dear . . . we'll be right over. Goodbye. And thank you."

Benji watched indifferently as the man came out of the office and walked along between the cages. Then he jumped quickly to his feet and wagged his tail as the man smiled at him and unfastened the clasp on his cage.

"Well, Benji, you're going home." Benji barked, jumped up excitedly, and turned a quick circle as he headed toward the office with the man. When the door was opened he bolted through and then skidded to a stop.

"Well, hello, Benji. How are you, old chap?"

Is was the English couple!

It was a pleasant-looking place with deep carpets and nice furniture. A stairway at the side seemed to lead up to a second floor and there was a kitchen off to the other side.

"Well, Benji," the man said, smiling down at him, "you seem to be quite a prize. I quite imagine you are the most valuable dog in all of Greece right now."

Benji gave the tall Britisher a puzzled look and began sniffing his way around the room.

"Come over here, Benji," the woman said from the couch. "Let's have a look at you."

Benji moved reluctantly to the couch and let the woman lift him to her lap. She scratched his back for a minute and then unfastened his collar.

"What on earth are you doing?" the man asked. He was across the room at a small bar, mixing drinks.

The woman squinted closely at Benji's collar, then pulled a magnifying glass from a drawer. "I am looking, darling. Of course, it would help if I knew what I was looking for."

The man laughed. "Sometimes you surprise me, Elizabeth. As pretty as you are, I never suspected you might also be intelligent."

"Why, thank you, Ronald."

"Did you really take that as a compliment? In that case, I'll take it back." The man brought a drink to the woman and smiled. "However, I will grant that your suggestion to check the dog pounds was unusually brilliant."

"Hmph. And I hope you realize that I won't be the only one to think of it." She put Benji's collar back on. "And with all the interest in Benji here, I suspect we'll soon be having visitors."

"I'm sure of it. It appears that our hideaway scientist has suddenly become a very important man."

"And very valuable." The woman smiled as she took a sip of her drink. "Let's just hope we get our share of the profits."

Benji felt his ear being lifted. The woman was peering into it was a magnifying glass, pulling the ear from one side to the other.

"Do you see anything?"

"Not a thing." Benji felt the ear drop and the woman frowned at him. "Benji, why can't you talk and give us a hint? You didn't swallow it, did you?"

Benji put his head down on her lap and looked off at the man. He still couldn't figure out if the two of them were friends. By the way they acted, they didn't seem to intend him any harm.

Benji closed his eyes, enjoying the back rub, then he jerked his head up as the doorbell suddenly rang.

The man smiled faintly and glanced at the door. "I say, it appears to be starting already." He put his drink on the table and quickly picked up Benji. "I'll take Mr. Popular upstairs and we'll make a few photographs. All right, Benji?" He glanced at the woman as he headed for the stairs. "Give me a moment to prepare, darling. Then get rid of them."

Benji glanced at the door, but it was quickly out of sight as they went up the stairs and into a bedroom. The man shut the door and put Benji down, hurrying off to a dresser. He brought out a fancy-looking camera and studied it for a minute. Then he crossed to a couch under a window. He pushed the window open wide and leaned out, the camera lifted to his eye.

"I'm sorry, they must be mistaken," the woman's voice echoed clearly up from the porch below. "We haven't been to the dog pound, and we don't have a dog."

"This is your name and address, isn't it?" a man's voice questioned. "Maybe your husband picked up the dog." The voice was deep and a little harsh. Benji didn't recognize it at all.

"No, I'm afraid that is impossible," the woman answered. "You see, my husband hates dogs."

Ronald smiled when he heard that. "Don't you believe it, Benji," he said softly. "Some of my best friends are dogs."

Benji stared at the man and cocked his head, listening to the voices downstairs again.

"I see," the man at the door was saying. "Well, thank you very much."

The door clicked shut and Benji moved across the room and jumped up on the couch next to the Englishman.

"Now," the man said, squinting into his camera, "just turn around, please, so I can have a look at your face."

Out the window, Benji could see the man as he walked down the steps and opened the door of a station wagon. He was wearing an Olympic Airways uniform, and his car had an airline insignia on the door.

The man glanced back at the apartment house and the camera clicked again.

"Ahhh," the Englishman said, "thank you very much." It was a perfect picture. The man was a thick-necked Greek with cold dark eyes. It was Stelios.

"What do you think?" said the Englishman, dropping back on the couch. "Was the gentleman really from Olympic Airways?" He smiled and put a cover over the lens of the camera. "I wouldn't want to bet on it. But we have him nicely recorded. That should be worth something."

The man put the camera on the dresser and Benji trotted alongside as he went to the door.

"No, no. I'm afraid you'll have to stay here, Benji." The man smiled and opened the door only wide enough to squeeze through.

Benji watched it shut and then scratched at the bottom and barked. Why did he have to stay in the room? He scratched again and gave a loud bark.

The door opened, but only a few inches, with the man blocking Benji's escape. "Here, here," he said, "we'll have none of that."

Benji barked again.

"No," the man said. He reached down, turned him around, and gave him a whack on the rear. "Now you might just as well make yourself comfortable, because this is going to be your home for a while."

Benji watched the door close again.

Locked in the room, there was nothing he could do. Until somebody opened the door, or took him out for a walk, he might as well make the best of it. He glanced, sniffed a couple of things and finally jumped back on the couch. He found a soft pillow in the corner and curled up, gazing emptily down at the carpet. He finally sighed and closed his eyes.

As he drifted off to sleep he heard a car door slam, and moments later the doorbell rang.

"Yes?" the Englishwoman's voice said.

"How do you do?" It was a woman's voice. "I'm here about the dog you picked up at the pound today."

Benji's eyes popped open. Was he dreaming, or had he heard a familiar voice? No, he wasn't dreaming. It was Mary. Or at least it sounded like Mary. He jumped onto the windowsill and listened closely.

"I'm sorry," the Englishwoman was saying irritably. "Somebody seems to have made a stupid mistake, and I wish whoever it was would correct it."

Benji stretched out the window, straining to see below, but the porch roof and an awning made it impossible to see the apartment door.

"You're the second person to ask about this," the Englishwoman said, "but we do not have a dog. We have never had a dog, and we did not pick up a dog at the pound today."

Benji looked toward the street where a huge truck was making a loud racket as it climbed slowly up the hill. He could hardly hear the voices anymore.

". . . and my husband hates dogs, so you see . . ."

Benji jumped from the couch and ran to the door, scratching at it again. He barked a few times, but the noise of the truck was growing so loud he was certain no one could hear him. He raced back to the couch and bounded up with his front paws on the windowsill. Then his heart jumped and he almost tumbled out the

For The Love of Benji

The New Adventure of America's Most Huggable Hero

BENJI

The plotters meet.

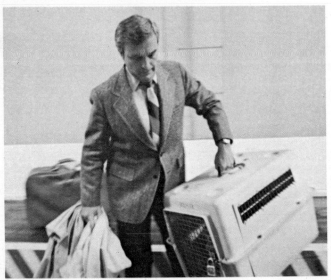

Chandler Dietrich makes his move.

Benji escapes.

Lost in Athens.

Looking for lunch.

Food at last!

The getaway.

Trapped!

Looking for a way out.

Jumping to safety.

Chandler is close behind.

He captures Benji...

...But not for long.

Protected by a friend.

Reunited with the family...

But Chandler returns…

...And Tiffany.

...And gets Benji again.

Benji waits for a chance to escape.

Free of Chandler, he heads back to the family.

Why is their hotel surrounded by police?

Chandler is holding Cindy hostage...

...While Mary and Paul look on anxiously.

It's a dangerous moment when
Benji comes to the rescue.

Chandler's dognapping days are over.

Now everyone can enjoy their vacation in
Greece—including the new father.

Photographs by Shelly Katz

window as he barked as loud and urgently as he could.

It was Mary! She was walking across the street to a taxi and the driver was holding the door open for her. Benji yelped frantically, his back feet on top of the couch and his front on the windowsill.

He saw the cab door shut and then the big truck was passing, the roar of its big diesel motor drowning out every other sound. But Benji continued barking, leaning far out the window as the taxi pulled out a little and the driver waited for the truck to go by. He barked and barked, putting all the urgency and desperation he could into his voice.

"Benji!" a voice behind him cried.

Benji looked back, almost losing his balance as he turned. Ronald, the Englishman, was just inside the door, moving toward him. He smiled uneasily and came closer. "Now, Benji, just take it easy."

Benji looked out at the street again. The taxi was pulling away from the curb, starting to move slowly up the hill. Benji barked again and again, hoping by some miracle Mary might look out the back window.

"Don't be afraid, Benji," the man behind him said as he came closer, "I'll get you down. Just don't move. That's a good boy."

Benji looked from the cab to the man and back at the cab again. It was halfway to the corner now and behind him the man was getting close. He looked down at the sloped awning eight feet below and hesitated.

"Benji!" the man cried out and lunged for him. Benji jumped.

The canvas awning sagged enough that it was like a net breaking his fall. But the slope was steep and Benji skidded and tumbled, unable to get his footing after he hit. Then he was over the edge, his legs groping at empty air for a minute before he crashed into a heavy shrub.

"Benji!" the Englishman shouted from the window, but Benji didn't bother looking back. He squirmed out of the shrub and was running at full speed when he hit the ground and dashed into the street.

Suddenly, there was a loud screech of tires and Benji swerved, just missing the front wheel of a small red sports car being driven recklessly by a distinguished-looking man in a dark suit. It was Chandler Dietrich. Benji bolted past the car and kept going, his legs flying and his feet hardly touching the pavement as he raced for the corner at the top of the hill.

Dietrich immediately threw the car into reverse, the gears grinding loudly. Before he could whip the car around he found himself in the middle of three other cars, all trying to go in the other direction. He groaned and beat his fist against the dash.

When Benji rounded the corner he could see the taxi picking up speed a block ahead of him. He ran faster, his eyes fixed on the back of the car, his heart pounding wildly.

The taxi was growing smaller and smaller, finally disappearing in the traffic as it sailed along the boulevard. Benji slowed to a trot and finally stopped.

He gazed forlornly at the street for a while and then moved to the sidewalk. He sat down and panted, watching the pedestrians go by.

V

At the end of the alley Benji stopped and surveyed the big cross street. Then he frowned, staring at a taxi waiting for a signal. He could just see the head of someone in the back seat. Could it be Mary? He moved quickly along the sidewalk. He ducked between two parked cars and got up on his hind legs, trying desperately to see into the back seat of the taxi.

The woman in the taxi looked at him through the window and blinked. It was not Mary. The cab moved on, pulling away with the rest of the traffic.

Benji saw a great deal of Athens that he hadn't seen before. There were several large parks in front of huge buildings, and he picked up a few of the tidbits that people were feeding to pigeons. But the people didn't seem to like the idea of his scaring the birds and taking their food, so he trotted on, watching the taxis and the people walking along the streets.

He had just rounded a corner and was enjoying the smells of a huge outdoor flower shop when he almost ran squarely into the two policemen. They were standing by the curb quietly talking and laughing. Benji made a sharp turn and ducked behind a big flowerpot. He stayed there for five minutes before he finally crept out and headed the other way, moving cautiously. He was glancing back to make certain the two men weren't following him when he suddenly banged into another pair of legs. He froze for an instant as he looked up. The legs belonged to a third policeman.

The man smiled and said something to him and then reached down as if to pet him. But since Benji's recent experiences with policemen had been none too pleasant, he didn't take any chances. Before the policeman's hand was anywhere close, Benji ducked and took off at full speed, tearing around the corner and disappearing up the first alley he came to.

As Benji rounded the corner he saw, across the street, a huge building with hundreds of windows. In front of it, a constant flow of taxis kept loading and unloading people. Benji stopped and took a closer look as three people emerged from the taxi nearest the door.

It was them! Benji was sure of it this time. He had a clear glimpse of Cindy carrying Tiffany, and then Paul and Mary following her through the revolving doors.

Benji moved quickly through the parked cars and watched for a break in traffic. Then he bolted across and raced at full speed toward the hotel door.

He didn't notice the man leaning into the window of the cab giving something to the driver until the man turned toward the hotel entrance. Both Benji and the man came to an abrupt stop.

It was Dietrich.

The man glanced at the revolving door through which Mary, Paul, and Cindy had just disappeared. Then an ever-so-slight smile spread across his lips and he began moving toward Benji. Benji looked nervously at the revolving door, then back to Dietrich.

"Come on, Benji," he said. He bent forward a little, holding his hand out. "Come on, boy, I'm not going to hurt you."

Benji remembered his first experience with Chandler Dietrich and moved a few steps back glancing at the door again. He barked at the man, trying to show he was not interested in his friendship. But Dietrich kept coming, moving a little faster now. Benji turned and trotted four or five steps away and looked back. Then Dietrich lunged for him and Benji was at the corner and across the street in seconds.

Dietrich stopped short of the corner and stood staring at Benji, a thoughtful look on his face. He smiled faintly and moved back toward the hotel door.

Benji heard the clank of a garbage can being opened. He stopped and peered up a long dark alley.

A round-faced man wearing an apron was singing and emptying smaller buckets of garbage into the big can. Benji stood still, watching quietly. Then the man saw him. He smiled and said something that sounded friendly, but Benji didn't move.

The man put the lid back on the can. Then he knelt down and smiled again, this time holding his hand out as he spoke. Benji still didn't move, although the man's smile was reassuring. Benji's stomach was starting to twist and grumble again.

Finally, he began to move slowly, glancing behind him once or twice, ready to run if he had to. As Benji got closer, the man suddenly rose and took a step forward. Benji quickly turned and retreated, watching the man carefully.

The man seemed to understand. He squatted down and held his hand out again, showing Benji an open palm. His voice sounded sympathetic and he spoke quietly.

Benji still wasn't too sure. He tensed as the man rose again. This time the man opened the big garbage can and came out with a tasty looking scrap of meat. He laughed and squatted again, holding it out to Benji.

This was more like it. Benji wagged his tail and moved cautiously forward. He stopped a few inches short of the meat and sniffed it. Then he couldn't resist; he stepped forward and took it, gulping it down.

The man talked quietly as he patted Benji's head. Benji wagged his tail and then hesitated as the man rose and opened the screen door at the back of the building. But the smells coming from inside were so delicious that Benji gave in easily. He wagged his tail and moved inside, glancing cautiously around.

It was a big kitchen, apparently at the back of a restaurant. Benji relaxed a little and gave the man a panting smile as he watched him get a big bowl from a cupboard. The man laughed and talked and put a handful of meat scraps in the bowl. Then he filled another bowl with water and placed them both on the floor.

It seemed like the best meal Benji had ever had and when he finished the first bowl the man filled it up again. Then he had a good drink of water.

The man wasn't watching him anymore. He was standing at a big stove, pouring something from one huge pot into another and stirring the whole thing. Benji sniffed around the kitchen a little and finally settled down in a corner.

The man smiled at him a couple times, but made no move to turn Benji out. That was fine with Benji. For the present he wanted nothing more than a safe, warm place to catch up on his sleep, and it looked like he had found it. He took a last look around and settled his head comfortably on the floor, closing his eyes with a weary sigh.

When Benji appeared to be comfortably asleep, the restaurant owner smiled pleasantly at him and moved to the wall phone in the corner of the kitchen.

He said something Benji didn't under-stand, and hung up the phone and walked through the door to the restaurant.

Benji looked up sharply as he heard the door swing shut. He glanced around the kitchen assuring himself that he was alone, and closed his eyes again. He thought dreamily about Mary and Paul and Cindy and imagined him-self sitting with them on a lazy afternoon in Silver Creek. Then Benji slept soundly.

Benji lifted his head and blinked around. He heard a loud snarl. He stared at the dirty window above his head and instantly jumped to his feet.

A huge, black, vicious-looking dog was looking straight at Benji, his pointed teeth snapping against the window. And behind him, squinting and shading his eyes, was Chandler Dietrich.

The screen door creaked open and clicked softly shut again and there was the rustle of footsteps.

"I know you're in here, Benji boy," Die-trich said softly.

Dietrich paused to let his eyes adjust to the dimly lit room. He looked down to the spot where Benji had been sitting, but there was only an empty bowl. "Come on, Benji. You don't want me to bring that Doberman in here, do you?"

Dietrich walked toward the cupboard. His

arm brushed against a broom and it clattered to the floor.

"Come on, Benji. Be a good boy."

He threw open the closet door and quickly slammed it shut. "Why are you afraid of me, Benji? I've never hurt you. Don't you want to see your friends again?"

He paused again. There was no sign of Benji. "Come on Benji. Here, Benji," the voice continued in its soft singsong.

Dietrich cast a puzzled look around the room, then knelt to open the last door of the cupboard.

"Come on, Ben—!"

Like a gunshot, Benji sprang forward, crashing into Dietrich's face and knocking him backward.

Dietrich let out a cry and was on his back as Benji scampered over his legs, going directly for the screen door. Benji lifted his front paws in mid-flight and the door sprang open; he plummeted through it.

If the Doberman had been expecting him, Benji probably wouldn't have had a chance to get by. The big black dog was tied to a post just outside the door, and when Benji came flying out his head brushed by just under the Doberman's chin. By the time the big black animal had recovered from the surprise, Benji was halfway down the alley and taking the corner at full speed.

Benji ran for three blocks before he finally slowed down and took a glance behind. He could see no one following him, but he kept moving anyway.

Whenever there was a break in traffic he crossed the street, and then crossed again, hoping to leave the vicious black dog behind him for good.

It was getting dark now, and Benji finally headed back toward the ruins. It had been a long day and he couldn't keep moving forever.

The place looked as dark and lonely as ever. Moving through the ruins he circled a few statues and took a roundabout route getting to the wall and going up through the graveyard.

His friend, the big brown dog, wasn't there. An old, well-chewed bone lay in the corner of the nook. Benji sniffed at it, and then just to make sure about things he climbed up on the hill behind the nook and looked over the graveyard and the ruins below. There seemed to be nobody around, particularly no giant black dogs.

Benji went back down to the nook and made himself comfortable, his eyes fixed absently on the graveyard below. He thought of little Tiffany and wished they had never left Silver Creek. He finally sighed and gazed dully across the graveyard for a few minutes. Then he was fast asleep.

Benji's eyes popped open, and he froze, not daring to move. He was certain he had heard something. He came cautiously to his feet, watching, scanning the ruins beyond the wall. All the dark shapes and shadows now looked ominous, like people and dogs and animals holding themselves still, waiting for him to look the other way.

The graveyard looked even more frightening. Benji hadn't thought much about it when he walked through there in the daylight. But now he was certain he could see thin shadows moving around and hovering over gravestones. He stared, moving his gaze slowly across the dark shapes. Then his heart leaped into his throat and he jumped to the side as a small rock clattered to the ground just behind him.

He froze in his tracks and looked up. High on the wall, the silhouette of a big dog was clearly outlined against the sky and he could see the pale glint of white teeth. Benji looked quickly around, searching for Dietrich, but he could see no other distinct shadows.

Benji backed slowly, almost tiptoeing into a corner of the nook, just under the ledge. More gravel suddenly poured down from above and he tightened himself closer against the wall, pulling his tail close to his side.

There was a heavy *thunk* on the ledge above him. Then he saw the shape land on the ground just beside him. His muscles went limp with relief.

It was his friend. The big brown dog was turning slowly around, looking things over, giving the old bone a sniff. Benji panted and barked softly, saying hello, and stretched out on his stomach.

The dog swung his head over and nudged Benji, giving his face a half lick. He circled a couple of times and made himself comfortable.

Then Benji went back to sleep feeling much more secure with his friend at his side.

VI

At dawn, Benji returned to the hotel and watched the entrance most of the morning. He stayed across the street for awhile, keeping out of sight behind lampposts and telephone poles. He saw no one who looked like Mary, Paul, or Cindy, and nobody brought Tiffany out for a walk.

He considered the idea of marching up to the revolving door and just trotting inside. But there was a uniformed doorman constantly moving back and forth helping people out of cabs and calling other cabs for people coming out of the hotel. He waited, hoping the man would leave for a while. When he finally did, the man who took his place looked meaner than the first one.

Benji finally crossed the street. A narrow stretch of grass with bushes behind it ran along the front of the hotel, and he could lie near the bushes, half hidden from most of the people walking by. He spent another hour there, taking time out only to trot four blocks down the street to a big fountain and have himself a drink. When he got back things looked the same. He finally rose and trotted a little closer to the door, quickly dropping to the ground when the doorman looked in his direction.

He waited as the man opened the cab doors and whistled for empty cabs to stop. Then, staying low to the ground, he scooched up another few feet. The man glanced in his direction, but didn't seem particularly interested.

Benji watched as a taxi with five people and a lot of suitcases stopped. The doorman opened the cab doors and then whistled for some bellhops to help with the luggage. They were all gathered around as the doorman shouted instructions. Benji trotted casually forward.

An empty section of the revolving door was coming slowly around. Benji watched carefully as a woman and two men pushed their way through the door, sending it into a rapid spin. They made it look so simple. Benji cocked his head, made one false start, then headed straight for the door.

"*Aaiieee!*" someone shouted behind him. Benji skidded to a stop.

The doorman frowned, stomped his foot loudly against the marble pavement, and started toward Benji.

Benji trotted a few steps and looked back. But the man was still watching him. He shouted again, suddenly moving quickly forward. Benji turned and ran.

As Benji sniffed at the screen door and peered inside the kitchen seemed to be empty. He barked and waited, then barked again. No one came.

The door was slightly ajar and Benji studied it for a minute. He scratched at it, but it didn't budge. He crawled close to it on his stomach, working at it with his nose. It finally opened enough to get a paw inside, and he squeezed through.

The cupboards were all closed again and three or four big pots were simmering on the stove. Benji tried the swinging door, scratching at it, then rising and pushing with all his weight. It opened just enough for Benji to squeeze through.

The inside part of the restaurant was also empty. The tables were all set with napkins and silver, but there were no customers. Benji trotted across the room and stopped in the open doorway to look around. There were tables everywhere . . . on the sidewalks, even *in* the street itself. But they were all empty. All except one across the street.

Benji's tail started wagging. It was his friend with the apron who had fed him the day before. He was talking to a second man, a large Greek with black hair and cold dark eyes. Benji didn't seem to remember him, maybe because the last time he had seen him, the man had been in an airlines uniform. It was Stelios.

Benji watched for a break in traffic, then

trotted across to the other curb, wagging his tail as he approached the table.

They didn't see him. The man with the apron was leaning across the table, talking in a low voice. The dark Greek was nodding and gazing off in the other direction, his eyes half closed. Benji sat down and barked.

Suddenly he was off the ground, his bark choked off by the tight grip around his chest.

It was Dietrich again, and he was acting most unfriendly. Benji squirmed and yelped, trying to push and scratch with his paws, but the man was squeezing the breath out of him.

"Don't get up, gentlemen," Dietrich said, "just stay put."

The two men at the table stared at Dietrich, who was pointing a black pistol at them. Stelios looked tense, his hands resting near the edge of the table as if he was ready to jump. "You know your identity is no longer a secret," Stelios said coldly. "Give me the dog and I'll try to see that you come out of this alive."

"That is very considerate of you," Dietrich answered, "but I'll take care of that myself." He was edging toward the street now, glancing back at the traffic.

"You're going to be very sorry, my friend!"

There were no cars coming now and Dietrich laughed. "Good day, gentlemen." And he backed across the street with Benji. When he reached the curb he turned and ran into the café.

Before he reached the kitchen door he turned sharply between the tables and ducked behind a curtained partition that hid a row of coffeepots. Then Benji felt the man's hand suddenly grip his mouth, clamping it shut.

Through the partition Benji could see the other two men come jogging across the street. They separated as they reached the curb. The man with the apron disappeared around the side of the building as Stelios moved cautiously to the door and peered in. Benji felt Dietrich's hand tighten painfully around his throat.

Benji watched, struggling to get some air. Stelios came quickly through the door, glancing around the empty tables. As he crossed to the kitchen door Dietrich squeezed himself and Benji tight around the wall. Stelios didn't look around. He stood at the kitchen door for a minute, listening. Then he pushed it open and disappeared. In the alley, Benji heard a noise that caused him to freeze; it was the vicious barking of Dietrich's huge dog.

Benji heard a chuckle from Dietrich as he headed for the door. His hand was still tight around Benji's nose. When they were out on the sidewalk and striding up the street, Benji struggled again, trying to get air.

"Sorry, Benji," Dietrich said and eased his grip a little. "Just a bit farther."

Dietrich walked a little slower now, trying not to attract attention. He turned a corner and headed toward the end of the alley.

Dietrich's red sports car was parked at a nearby curb. He shifted Benji to the other arm and groped in his pocket for the keys. Suddenly, there was a low snarling sound from behind him and Dietrich spun around. The huge black Doberman was galloping toward him at a terrifying speed, his eyes fixed on Benji.

"No, it's OK!" shouted Dietrich.

The angry red eyes and the glistening teeth kept coming. Benji struggled, trying to spring away from Dietrich.

"Stay!" Dietrich commanded. There was a note of fear in his voice as he backed away, edging along the side of the car. *"Stay!"* he shouted again.

The dog ignored him. His gaze was locked on Benji and he came even faster, then he leaped through the air. Benji struggled free as Dietrich threw up his arms to protect his face and they all crashed down onto the sidewalk.

Dietrich landed on his back and the Doberman skidded past, his legs splayed out in all directions. Benji tumbled over, miraculously landing on his feet and in a flash he was running at full speed back down the alley.

Benji had a head start but he knew he was in great danger. He threw a quick glance behind him as he rounded the first corner. The Doberman was coming, galloping along the parked cars and beginning to pick up speed. Benji crossed another street and headed into an alley.

He could hear the yelps and snarls coming closer, and as he rounded the next corner Benji skidded, almost losing his footing as he made a second sharp turn down three steps which led to a closed door. He quickly fell against the door, hiding himself below the narrow street.

A second later the Doberman flashed by. Benji leaped back to the street level and took off in the opposite direction.

He had picked up another head start but he knew it wouldn't last long. Benji sped on, beginning to feel a little tired. He eased his pace a notch, panting, trying to recover some breath. Then he suddenly slid to a stop as he passed a high board fence.

There was a small hole at the bottom of the fence. He turned and saw the Doberman bearing down on him. He lowered his head and in a flash was through the hole and under the fence.

The Doberman's snout came through the hole. The big animal snarled and bared his teeth and shoved his head through the hole. But that was as far as he could get. He backed away and the sharp teeth sank into the wood.

Benji paused at the end of the alley to glance back over his shoulder. He saw the Doberman's head and front paws appear at the top of the fence. He could hear the animal scratching desperately with the claws of his back feet and then he dropped from sight again. Benji stared as the Doberman tried again, straining every muscle in his black, sleek body. This time he made it.

Benji ran as fast as his tired legs would carry him through the ruins and finally paused at the top of the hill and looked back. His heart sank as he saw the big Doberman bounding down the steps into the ruins.

He took a different route through the cemetery, climbing the hill on the side of his hideout. When he reached the top of the wall, just above the nook, he peered down hoping to see his old friend stretched out on the ground.

The nook was empty. And down in the cemetery the Doberman was coming, following the same route Benji had taken. Benji was panting, ready to collapse from exhaustion. He watched the big animal for a minute; then he jumped down to the ledge and dropped to the floor of the nook. He slid under the ledge and looked up, waiting for the inevitable. He knew he could not run anymore.

A minute later the Doberman appeared. He was standing high on the wall above, panting easily as he looked down. He took his time now, knowing Benji was trapped. He bounded easily down to the ledge and then to the floor, flashing his ugly teeth at Benji.

Then suddenly he stiffened. His head jerked to one side and his look of satisfied anticipation melted into one of fear. For there, under the ledge with Benji, was the big brown dog. The *very big* brown dog. He pulled himself up and began to move toward the Doberman, teeth bared, totally confident. The Doberman blinked and backed away until his rear bumped the wall behind him. Then, in a desperate leap, he went up the ledge and over the wall.

The big brown dog turned to look at his small frightened little friend, but by now Benji was far away, running . . . running through the narrow streets of Athens.

VII

Benji quietly circled around the two rosebushes, looking to see if the doorman was watching. Then he moved along more cautiously, crawling on his belly until he was within twenty feet of the door. He inched up the steps, pausing now and then to lift his head just high enough to look the situation over.

He saw several people going in and out, and then his ears popped up as he saw a door open off to the side. Two bellboys were coming through, pushing a big empty cart. Once they were out, the door swung shut and they rolled the cart off the curb.

The boys took suitcases from the roof of a big airport limousine and stacked them on the cart. A lot of people were getting out of the car and looking the hotel over while they moved toward the door. Benji watched and then looked at the bellboys again.

The cart was almost full now. One of the boys struggled to pull the last suitcase from the roof and finally wedged it into the top of the load. The doorman was bent forward talking to the driver of the limousine, and Benji glanced quickly at the revolving door. It was crowded with people waiting their turns to go through. He sighed and looked at the cart again.

It was coming toward the door now, one of the boys pulling and the other pushing from behind. Benji watched carefully. The bags were stacked high above the bellboys' heads. Benji glanced at the door and then off toward the limousine. The doorman was still bent forward talking to the driver. Suddenly Benji lifted his head. He scooched forward a little, never taking his eyes from the baggage cart.

The cart was about to pass within a few feet of him. Impulsively, Benji trotted across and fell easily into step with the cart. He walked as close to the center of the cart as he could, completely hidden from the doorman on the other side. The boy in front opened the door as they creaked slowly forward. Benji held his breath as they moved inside.

He passed a large plant, then a row of soft chairs with two or three people sitting in them. A man looked at him and smiled and then went back to reading his newspaper. Then the cart stopped and Benji stopped with it.

One of the bellboys walked over to the desk while the other one leaned on the luggage, staring out at nothing. Benji drew his head back and twisted himself around to face the other way. He could see several elevators and a glass door leading to a coffee shop. No sign of Mary, Paul, or Cindy. He glanced up and blinked.

The bellboy was staring down at him and

frowning as if he couldn't believe his eyes. Then he cried out and made a lunge for Benji.

The floor was slippery, but Benji got his feet going just in time. The boy half stumbled and then lit out after him. Benji kept going, racing across the slick marble floor. There were two bellboys chasing him now, both of them yelling.

Benji's feet hardly touched the ground as he headed for the broad stairway which descended steeply to the coffee shop. Benji took the stairs much quicker than the two bellboys, who stumbled down behind him.

Suddenly Benji heard a familiar voice cry out and his head whipped sharply around.

"Benji!"

It was Cindy, standing just outside the coffee shop, still holding the door open. "Mary! Paul! Benji is here!" she shouted behind her.

Benji couldn't recall ever having moved so fast. He wasn't too sure if he even took any steps. It seemed like he made one giant leap and flew twenty feet across the floor into Cindy's arms.

And then Paul and Mary were coming through the door and Benji was licking Cindy's face and then Paul's and then Mary's as they all crowded around him.

For a few minutes he didn't even notice the bellboys standing in the lobby watching. Mary, Paul, and Cindy were all grinning and talking at once, all of them hugging him and getting their faces licked. Then Mary's face suddenly became very serious and she turned to face the perspiring spectators.

"Thank you very much," she said as if she were dismissing servants, "You may go now."

Tiffany had never looked more beautiful. She was freshly groomed, every hair meticulously in place. Benji couldn't resist a happy bark as he trotted across the hotel room. He gave her nose a gentle nudge and licked her face affectionately.

Cindy laughed and Mary wondered aloud how Benji had ever managed to find *them* when they had looked all over Athens without finding *him*. Mary walked over to close the open door which led to the hall when she stopped abruptly and stepped back from the door.

A man with a heavy jacket was standing in front of her. Benji came instantly to his feet when he got a look at him. It was Stelios.

"Yes?" Mary said, surprised.

The man didn't answer immediately. He moved a couple of feet into the room and his narrowed eyes quickly found Benji. Then he looked at Cindy and Mary and glanced suspiciously at the bathroom door.

"I need to borrow your dog for a few days," he said gruffly. "The brown one on the couch there."

It was neither a question nor a polite request. With his grim face and the cold hard eyes the man looked like he was accustomed to issuing orders and having them obeyed without question.

Paul and Cindy flashed a puzzled look at Mary. "I beg your pardon," she said.

"The dog," the man said. "I need to borrow him for a few days."

Mary blinked incredulously at him. "I don't understand. Who are you, and what are you talking about?"

The man looked slightly uneasy, as if he was suddenly aware that his rough manner had startled everybody. He glanced at Benji again and shook his head. "Belive me, it's at least partly for the dog's own safety, lady. He'll be returned unharmed in a day or two."

"I still don't know what you are talking about," Mary said. She gave the man a hard stare.

"All right, lady . . ." The man reached for his back pocket.

Several things happened at that moment. Chandler Dietrich suddenly appeared behind the man and Benji barked as quickly as he saw him. Mary noticed him too, and with a look of relief she said, "Oh, Chandler, I'm . . ."

At that moment the Greek whirled around, and Dietrich struck him hard with the butt of his pistol.

"Chandler!" Mary cried out as the man crashed to the floor.

Benji was barking; partly at Dietrich and partly from surprise. He sat very close to Cindy, looking from Dietrich to the man on the floor.

Paul moved toward Mary and she reached protectively as she gaped at Dietrich. "Chandler, why on earth did you do a thing like that?! What in heaven's name is going on?"

"It's all right, Mary," Dietrich said. He took a quick look at the fallen man and moved across the room. "Now don't worry. Everything's going to be all right, I promise." He put his pistol in Mary's hand. "Just keep this pointed toward him and call the police. OK?"

Mary gaped at the pistol and back at Dietrich. "It most certainly is not OK! I don't like guns, and I want to know what this is all about, Chandler!"

Dietrich had moved back to the man and was going through his pockets. "I can't say right now." He found a wallet and stood up as he glanced through the contents. "I'm sorry, Mary," he said as he stuck the wallet in his jacket pocket. "I just can't tell you anything about it right now. Please trust me."

"Trust you for what?"

Dietrich hesitated. "It has to do with Benji. I have to take him for a couple of days."

"Why?" Cindy asked. "What's he done?"

"He hasn't done anything, Cindy, and I'll take good care of him. I promise."

"If he hasn't done anything, why do you want to take him?" Paul asked.

"And why did that man want to take him?" Mary added.

Dietrich chewed his lip for a minute and

then paced across the room to the window. "Mary," he finally said, "I work for the United States government, and Benji is the key to a very important situation. It's my fault he's involved in all this, and I'm sorry. I had no idea it would become this complicated." He shrugged. "But it has, and I'm afraid that's all I can say."

"Is Benji a spy?" Paul asked.

Dietrich gave a short laugh. "No, he's not a spy, Paul. But he is very important to the United States government right now."

"Hey, that's neat. You mean he'll be famous?"

"It is not neat," Cindy said.

Benji cocked his head, looking from one to the other.

"No, you're right, Cindy," Dietrich said. "It's not neat. But he is important. And necessary. OK?"

"What did he do?" Cindy asked, still not convinced. "Why is he important?"

Dietrich took a deep breath and sighed. "Honey, I just can't tell you right now. I'll explain the whole thing when I bring him back. OK?"

Paul and Mary looked doubtful, but Dietrich smiled at Cindy and waited for an answer. She looked glumly at Benji and finally nodded.

"Good girl," Dietrich said. "And I'm sorry, Mary."

"That's OK—I guess. Just take good care of him."

"I will. Now hurry and call the police. And if the man wakes up be sure to keep the gun on him."

"But I don't know anything about guns," Mary protested.

"All you have to know is to keep it pointed at him. He won't bother you."

Benji didn't like any part of what was going on. He watched warily as Dietrich came toward him.

Benji tried to get away, but Dietrich suddenly had him by the chest and lifted him. "I think you'll all be very proud of him," he said as he carried Benji to the door. "And I'll see you in a few days."

"Poor Benji," Cindy said as the door closed.

Paul smiled and shook his head as Mary picked up the phone again. "How about that? Benji's a spy."

"He is not a spy," Cindy protested.

"I'll bet that guy's a spy too," Paul said nodding at the man on the floor. Then he caught his breath. The man's hand was moving to his head and he was trying to pull himself up. "Mary?" cried Cindy and Paul in unison.

Mary looked and quickly clamped the phone between her shoulder and chin, holding the pistol out with both hands.

"Stay exactly where you are," she said striving to keep her voice under control. "Paul and Cindy, go around behind the bed."

The man was up on one knee, rubbing his

head. He blinked and looked around the room as if not certain where he was for a minute.

"Hello?" Mary said on the phone. "Yes. Will you please send the police to room seven-oh-one. Yes, that's right, the police. Thank you." She fumbled the receiver back to the cradle.

The man was on his feet now, frowning at Tiffany on the bed. "Where's the other dog? The brown one?"

"He's safely away from here," Mary said. She lifted the gun higher, pointing it directly at the man's chest.

The man's eyes narrowed. "Is he with Chandler Dietrich? Is that who hit me?"

"That doesn't happen to be any of your business," Mary answered. "Just stay there by the door and don't come any closer." The man had not moved, but she wasn't taking any chances.

The man snorted. "I suppose he told you he's an agent of the United States government."

"I told you, it's none of your business."

The man nodded and stepped forward. "Yes, it is my business, lady. You see, the body of the real Chandler Dietrich was found this morning at the bottom of a river in New Jersey. The man who was here is not Chandler Dietrich and he is not an agent for the United States government. Now please put that gun down so I can go after him."

Mary kept the gun up, not sure what to think. She had seen enough of Chandler Dietrich to know him fairly well, and he certainly seemed trustworthy. She didn't know anything about this man, and his appearance certainly did not inspire confidence. "And I suppose you're going to tell me you *are* an agent?"

The man sighed and shrugged. "What else?"

"I don't believe you," Mary answered promptly.

The man gave her a cold glance and turned away in frustration. "Well, we can wait for the police, and wait another hour for them to check it out. By then your Dietrich impostor can be halfway to Saudi Arabia."

It was clear that the man was getting impatient with her, and Mary wondered what she would do if he just walked out the door. If he did, she knew she couldn't pull the trigger. But she also wondered if he might be telling the truth. If he was, she could never forgive herself if Benji got hurt. She swallowed hard, keeping the gun up, at the same time trying to come to some kind of intelligent decision.

"Of course, it's not terribly important," the man said sarcastically. "I'm just trying to save the life of a top scientist, and preserve a project of worldwide significance. It's no big deal, lady."

Mary blinked, wondering if that was true. She knew about the scientist and how all the Athens police were looking for the man. But that didn't mean this man was on the side of the police.

"Well, say something!" the man suddenly shouted at her.

"I don't know what to say," replied Mary, on the verge of tears.

"Well, you can try saying goodbye to your dog, because that man who took him out of here will probably kill him when he's through."

Paul and Cindy moved closer to Mary, both of them blinking at the man. "I can't believe that," Mary said. "Chandler Dietrich is a very nice man."

"Don't you understand what I've been trying to tell you, lady? The man who has been traveling with you and escorting you around is *not* Chandler Dietrich! He's an international thief, and he's probably a murderer! And what your dog probably has tattooed somewhere on his body is worth nothing to him if anyone else gets their hands on it. Now, if he's killed a person, is he going to stop with a little . . . brown . . . dog?"

Mary crumbled into tears and Stelios grabbed the gun.

"I'm sorry I had to say those things," Stelios said. "But you won't be." Mary didn't know what to say. She felt a little ill.

The man looked at them for a minute and then disappeared out the door.

VIII

Dietrich kept looking in the rearview mirror as he drove through the city. Benji sat tensely on the seat, watching the streets and wondering where they were going. He'd never seen this part of the city before. Dietrich made a lot of quick turns into alleys and narrow streets and then accelerated sharply.

Benji sighed and settled down, not knowing what to think.

A few minutes later when he sat up and looked out the window again, Benji could see water and hundreds of boats moored in a harbor. It seemed to be where they were headed.

Dietrich parked the car, then, with Benji in arm, he hurried down a long pier where dozens of huge boats were moored. About halfway out he stopped and looked back, then moved up the gangplank of a big cabin cruiser.

"Well, Benji boy, we seem to have made it." He smiled and hurried to a cabin door.

Then a familiar voice stopped him cold. "Do you still plan to dispose of him?"

Dietrich spun around toward the back of the boat.

It was Ronald, the Englishman. He and Elizabeth appeared very comfortable in a pair of deck chairs sipping tall, cool drinks.

"The wife and I sort of like the little chap. We would be quite distressed to hear he was left at the bottom of the harbor."

"What are you doing here?" Dietrich asked angrily.

The Englishman rose and moved slowly across the deck. "Well, to be frightfully honest, old boy, we thought it might have crossed your mind to—as you say—run out on us."

"Run out on you? That's ridiculous. There's nothing to run out on."

Benji looked off at the woman, and then felt himself swung around as Dietrich opened the cabin door and shoved him inside. The door closed quickly behind him.

Benji didn't move for a minute. He glanced around at the fancy leather seats and the big table in the middle of the room. Outside, the two men were still talking.

"There's really no point in discussing it," Dietrich was saying. "You didn't complete your end of the bargain. You let him get away."

Benji moved away from the vent and circled around the table. There were cushioned seats along both sides of the room, with round windows just above them. Benji jumped up and pressed a paw against one of the windows. It was closed tight.

"Yes, of course," the Englishman was saying outside, "I do appreciate that full value was not received. Still in all, a partnership is like a marriage, you know. For better or for worse. And we *did* expose ourselves to enormous risks."

From the seat Benji looked around at the rest of the room. Then he jumped up on the table and studied the vent directly overhead.

"I suppose that's true," Dietrich agreed. "However, as I said, you did not deliver the goods."

The Englishman's voice was still casual. "I do hope this is not going to be a problem," he said. "Having become involved in a project like this, of course, could be very costly to us. I should hate to think we might have to recover the costs in other ways."

Benji couldn't reach the vent. He tried two or three times but he could get only his nose that high. He finally gave it up and stared back at the door for a minute.

"Well," Dietrich said after a silence, "I guess you deserve something for your efforts. Shall we say a compromise? Ten percent instead of twenty?"

"Under the circumstances I suppose that's a fair turn. What do you think, dear?"

"I think it's quite honorable of Mr. Thompson."

"Shall we go inside and have a drink on it?" Dietrich said.

"Excellent idea," the Englishman answered.

Benji looked over at the row of windows

again and his eyes suddenly locked on one of the curtains. It was moving, flapping gently against a breeze from outside. Benji bounded quickly from the table and jumped to the cushioned seats, pushing the curtain aside with his nose. It was wide open! He peered out, then looked quickly back at the door.

Through the glass he could see a hand reaching for the knob. He pulled himself to the top and struggled through the window just as the door flew open behind him.

"By the way," the Englishman said, "you never did say what you intend to do with the dog."

Benji crept softly along the deck by the side of the cabin. He stopped short of the corner and peered cautiously up through a window.

"After I get the code from his foot," Dietrich said coldly, "the dog goes overboard."

Through the window Benji saw Dietrich step aside to let the couple pass. Then, without warning, Dietrich suddenly lifted a heavy brass telescope into the air. As it flashed forward Benji saw the Englishman disappear and heard a loud thump on the floor, followed quickly by another. Then there was only silence.

"And to keep the dog company," Dietrich chuckled, "the two of you can go overboard with him." Then the door slammed shut.

"Benji?" Dietrich said inside the cabin.

Benji looked behind him and saw Dietrich's head suddenly pop through the open window. "Benji!" he screamed.

Benji was over the railing and onto the pier in one bound. Behind him he could hear the clatter of Dietrich running through the cabin and throwing the door open. But Benji was on his way by then.

"Benji!" Dietrich screamed again.

Benji didn't glance back. He heard the thump of Dietrich jumping from the boat to the pier, and then the running footsteps. By that time Benji was almost to the end of the pier.

As he reached the top of the ramp he slowed to a stop and glanced around for an instant. Then he jumped to the side and looked back as splinters of wood seemed to explode within inches of his paw.

Dietrich was holding a heavy pistol with both hands, the ugly black barrel pointing directly at Benji. Benji was running at full speed when the next explosion came. He heard the loud bang, and at the same instant there was a click on the pavement just behind him and the bullet went whining into the distance.

Benji quickly altered his course, keeping a row of parked cars between himself and Dietrich. When he reached the top of the hill he looked back again. He saw the door slam on Dietrich's car and then it was backing up, the wheels spinning.

As Benji raced up the street in the general direction of town, he glanced back and saw

Dietrich's car. Benji made a sharp turn onto a long street. He heard the screech of tires as Dietrich turned the corner behind him.

Benji had no idea which street he should take to get back to familiar territory but he took a sharp left at the next corner. Behind him he heard the screech of tires from several cars and he glanced back, hoping one of them had blocked Dietrich's path.

Two cars were stopped crookedly in the intersection, but Dietrich had gotten by them and was still coming. He was gaining fast now. Benji rounded the corner.

As quickly as he was on the next street he skidded to a stop, his legs spinning under him. Then he turned and quickly went back to the corner, watching.

Dietrich took a wide angle, crossing all the way to the other side of the street before he came into the turn. His tires were screaming as he sped around the corner past Benji, then screeched to a stop as he saw Benji dash off in the opposite direction.

Benji heard more squealing of tires as he ran on at top speed. He knew the car would be gaining fast. The streets were more crowded now and Benji angled across a corner, tearing by several pedestrians and then between two parked cars. He suddenly felt more hopeful as he raced down the street and saw a broad flight of concrete steps leading off the sidewalk and up to the right. Benji bounded up the steps, taking them three at a time as he heard the car round the corner behind him.

When he reached the top he stopped to catch his breath, and then watched as Dietrich skidded to a halt on the street below. Benji stared at him and Dietrich stared back for a minute. Then Benji took off again, galloping easily along the higher street.

Had he lost him? Benji felt a little more confident now. He went up another set of steps and turned back in the opposite direction at the top. He slowed to a trot to catch his breath.

Then his heart dropped and he skidded to a stop again, staring off at the intersection ahead. Dietrich's red sports car was passing along the cross street. It screeched to a stop and the chase was on again.

Benji darted out, heading in the opposite direction from the car. There were more screeches behind him as Benji rounded the corner.

Up ahead six or seven garbage cans were standing in a cluster near the curb. Benji covered the distance in three seconds, sliding to a quick stop as he ducked in behind them. He stuck his nose out just enough to see the car coming around the corner. Then his eyes widened and his muscles tensed. He couldn't believe it for a minute. But it seemed to be true. Dietrich was coming faster and faster, and he was angling closer and closer to the curb, heading directly at him.

Benji spun and bolted out from between the cans an instant before the car soared over the curb. Then the cans exploded in every direction, sending garbage and trash splattering over the street and sidewalk. One of the lids sailed over Benji's head and went clattering off in front of him as he raced on at full speed.

He wasn't going to last a whole lot longer.

Suddenly, Benji saw a cobblestoned alley sloping up the hill to his right. Behind him he could hear brakes squealing as Dietrich slowed to make the turn. Benji bolted toward the alley and up the steps, finally disappearing around a corner.

Dietrich screeched to a halt at the bottom of the hill, jumped out and started up the steps. But it was no use. Benji was long gone. He gazed angrily toward the top of the hill for a long moment; then a smile began to spread slowly across his face. He hurried back to the car, slid behind the wheel, and disappeared into the afternoon traffic.

Things were beginning to look familiar again. Off in the distance Benji could see the ruins and the hill where he and his big friend had their hideout. He moved faster, wanting desperately to get back to Mary, Paul, and Cindy.

He galloped on through the park, sending dozens of pigeons flapping into the air. Then he rounded a corner and sped past the open flower market.

Only when Benji was within a block of the

hotel did he finally slow down a little. He rounded the corner and then came to an abrupt stop.

Traffic was blocked and at least a dozen police cars with flashing lights were parked in front of the hotel. Policemen were all over the place, some of them standing on the grass, others milling around the street or standing across from the hotel. There was a babble of noise from the car radios and the policemen seemed to have an awful lot of guns.

Benji moved along a few feet, trying to get a better view of things. But he still couldn't figure out what was going on. With all that crowd around, it was pretty clear that he would have no chance of sneaking in the door.

He turned and trotted back toward the corner and then stopped again.

Two policemen were standing side by side near the corner, staring directly at him. Benji looked out at the street. More policemen seemed to be coming in his direction, all of them moving slowly and watching him.

What was going on? Benji turned and trotted a few steps the other way and stopped again. Then his ears pricked up as a voice crackled over a loudspeaker echoing something in Greek.

The policemen were slowly closing in on him from all directions except the direction toward the hotel entrance. He was confused.

He finally turned and moved slowly toward the hotel. Then he stopped again and glanced around. The policemen behind him followed, always stopping within a few feet of him. And the ones in front of him seemed to edge back, clearing a path toward the hotel. Then he tensed, staring off at the entrance.

The revolving door was no longer turning. Two policemen stood on either side, huge guns held tightly in their hands.

"Προσοχη!" the loudspeaker repeated, the voice suddenly very soft. Benji glanced over at a man holding a microphone next to a police car. The man seemed to be looking directly at him as he spoke.

Then Benji saw them—Mary and Paul. They were staring at him from the far side of the hotel door, and they seemed to be holding tightly to each other as if they were frightened. Benji gave his tail an uncertain wag. Then he trotted forward, angling across the walk leading to the hotel door.

"BENJI!"

The voice was Cindy's, and it was a frightened, anguished scream that stopped Benji dead in his tracks.

Then he saw it—Dietrich's red sports car was at the curb about fifty feet away, with all the policemen standing well away from it.

Dietrich was behind the wheel and Cindy was sitting next to him. Benji's heart sank. Dietrich had an arm around Cindy's neck and tears were streaming down Cindy's face.

Then he saw something that gripped his entire body with an icy fear. In Dietrich's other hand, just inches from Cindy's head, was an ugly black piece of metal.

Benji's thoughts raced back to a dark night in Silver Creek when he'd seen another man hold a gun like that. He remembered the loud explosion, the flash of light, and the smell of gun-powder. And his friend falling to the side-walk.

"Benji?" Cindy called again weakly. "Here, Benji."

Benji stared for a full minute, scarcely breathing. Dietrich opened the car door and then tightened his grip on Cindy. Benji remem-bered Dietrich's attempts to shoot him and run him down with his car. Now he had Cindy. And a gun. Benji couldn't bear to see Cindy fall like his friend back in Silver Creek.

Suddenly Benji was in motion, gathering speed as he crossed the walk in front of the hotel. He could see Cindy's anguished look and the smile coming to Dietrich's face, and he was moving faster, digging in with each step, flying at full speed as he raced across the sidewalk. His eyes were fixed on only one thing—the ugly weapon resting in Dietrich's hand. The man was not going to make Cindy cry anymore and he was not going to harm her, and Benji didn't care what happened to him.

He was still ten feet from the car when he leaped, and for an instant he saw the look of doubt and fear cross Dietrich's face. Then Ben-ji was through the opened door and his teeth clamped into the man's bared wrist.

There was a yell as the impact sent Dietrich's arm high into the air and the gun exploded right next to Benji's ear, the bullet tearing harmlessly skyward. Then Dietrich's arm crashed down against the car door and the gun sailed free, clattering down onto the marble steps as Benji's momentum somersaulted him out of the car.

Benji scrambled to his feet, ready to run. But suddenly it was too crowded to run. A dozen policemen were now surrounding the car and rifles were being thrust through the doors on both sides.

It was over. The loudspeaker was blaring out instructions, more policemen were coming at full speed, and Benji edged back, trapped for a minute by the mass of surrounding legs. Then he spotted Mary and Paul and Cindy standing at the curb in front of the hotel. Mary was hugging Cindy, and Paul was looking off at the crowd around the car. Then a big smile suddenly came to his face.

"Benji!" he shouted. "Come on, Benji!"

And Benji did.

IX.

Benji had never seen a beach before. When they walked down from the hotel he stood looking at it for a long while, amazed at seeing so much empty sand in one place. He finally trotted to the shore and sniffed the clear, blue water, jumping back when the little waves broke and came chasing after him. Then he raced full speed along the edge, barking out at them, with Tiffany running along behind. The two of them finally jumped in and Benji leaped directly into the first wave that came along, showing off a little for Tiffany. She stayed in the shallow water and barked while he tumbled and thrashed around. Benji finally came back to shore and gave himself a good shake, looking things over again.

It was really a beautiful place. There were palm trees growing in the sand, and there wasn't another person or dog in sight for miles.

Paul and Cindy were in the water now and Benji watched them splash around and jump over the waves for a while. Up on the sand Stelios had strung a hammock between two palm trees and was stretched out in it while Mary sat in a beach chair under one of the trees, slowly swinging the hammock with one hand while fanning herself in the warm sun with the other.

"Benji just happened to be going to the right place at the right time, and for security reasons someone decided to let him carry the coordinate code for a secret meeting with the scientist," explained Stelios.

"Oh!" gasped Mary. "And we never caught on!" Then she said, "But why is the scientist so important?"

"They think he's close to a formula that'll turn one barrel of oil into twelve," Stelios replied. "You can guess how many folks would like to get their hands on that."

"Well," Mary sighed, "the whole thing sounds to me like something out of a James Bond movie."

Stelios laughed. "If it were a James Bond movie, I'd be Robert Redford and you'd be Genevieve Bujold." Mary grinned at the thought and Stelios continued. "Anyway, the whole thing would have worked if Benji hadn't missed the plane change in Athens."

Stelios paused, pushed back his straw hat, and gave Mary a wry smile.

"Hey, you're not living up to your part of the bargain. If I'm gonna talk, you've gotta pull."

Mary laughed and gave the hammock a

gentle tug. Behind her, Benji and Tiffany were still enjoying a romp in the cool surf.

"How did the man we thought was Dietrich find out about all this?" Mary continued.

"I don't know," replied Stelios casually. "Security leak, I guess. It happens all the time. We've got spies . . . they've got spies . . . and we're all trying to earn our salaries."

A big wave chased Benji and Tiffany back toward the beach, and they both took off in the direction of Paul and Cindy, who now sat on a blanket enjoying the ocean breeze.

"By the way, how's Benji?" asked Stelios as Benji and Tiffany trotted under the hammock. "Any signs of wear and tear?"

Mary turned to watch as Benji neared a large picnic basket and nudged the top away with his nose.

"I don't think Benji has ever been better," Mary answered simply.

Paul and Cindy smiled as Benji stood proudly looking into the basket. Inside were four of the handsomest, liveliest puppies they had ever seen. Three were cuddly white, with soft fine fur like their mother's. But the fourth . . . well, he was the obvious heir.

His mixed brown coat was scraggly with a little white streak on his chest and he yapped and growled as he crawled feistily over the other puppies.

Benji reached down into the basket, nudged him away from the others, and gingerly picked him up by the nape of the neck. The tiny puppy gave his proud father a small lick on the nose as Benji placed him carefully onto the blanket.

If ever a son bore the marks of his father, it was this lively, brown puppy who sat looking admiringly up at a very special dog named Benji.

Woof.